SOUNDS OF LANGUAGE

readers

Sounds of Children
   at Play on the Hill
Sounds Around the Mountain
Sounds of an Owly Night
Sounds of Home
Sounds of Numbers
Sounds Around the Clock
Sounds of a Powwow
Sounds of Laughter

SOUNDS
of Home

By Bill Martin Jr
with Peggy Brogan and
John Archambault

ISBN: 1–55924–363–5

1 2 3 4 5 6 7 8 9   96 95 94 93 92 91 90

Pictures by John Rombola

ACKNOWLEDGMENTS

Cover art by Kelly Oechsli.

"Daddy Is Home!" from DADDY IS HOME! by David Blomquist, Copyright © 1963 Frances Hooper.

"Round is a Pancake," from ROUND IS A PANCAKE by Joan Sullivan. A Little Owl Book, copyright © 1965 by Holt, Rinehart, Winston, Inc.

"How Many Apples?" picture adapted from the Young Owl book IF YOU CAN COUNT TO 10 by Howard F. Fehr, copyright © 1964 by Holt, Rinehart and Winston, Inc.

"Yes! We Have No Bananas" by Frank Silver and Irving Cohn. © 1923 Skidmore Music & Co., Inc., New York. Copyright Renewed. Used by permission.

"Dilly Dilly Piccalilli" (the text and illustrations) from FATHER FOX'S PENNYRHYMES by Clyde Watson, illustrated by Wendy Watson. (Crowell) Text Copyright © 1971 by Clyde Watson. Illustrations Copyright © 1971 by Wendy Watson. Reprinted by permission of Harper & Row, Publishers, Inc.

Thanks to Richard Erdoes for the photograph, "Little Sister."

Acknowledgment is made to Betty Jean Mitchell, for permission to use her character, Noodles © 1981.

Thanks to Linda Ross and Carol Misiaszek for their editorial and production assistance.

Every effort has been made to locate and secure permissions from the copyright holders for the stories used in this book. The publisher will be grateful if any omissions or errors are brought to their attention, so that they may be corrected.

picture by John Rombola

CONTENTS

SOUNDS OF HOME

Good Night, Mr. Beetle

by Leland B. Jacobs
pictures by Gilbert Riswold

Good night, Mr. Beetle,

Good night, Mr. Fly,

Good night, Mrs. Ladybug,

The moon's in the sky.

Good night, Mr. Rooster,

Good night, Mrs. Sheep,

Good night, Mr. Horse,

We must all go to sleep.

Good night, Miss Kitten,

Good night, Mr. Pup,

I'll see you in the morning

When the sun comes up.

All I Need

to make me happy
is three little kids
to call me pappy,
one named Ed,
and one named Fred,
and one named
Rebecca Ginger Bread.

an old rhyme adapted by Bill Martin Jr
drawings by Ray Barber

If I were a cat,

yes-sir-eeee!
I'd climb tip top
of the old pine tree.
Then I'd sit there and yowl
till everyone in town
came to watch the firefighters
get me down.

a poem by Noodles

"Pussy Cat, Pussy Cat
Where have you been?"
"I've been to London
To visit the Queen."

a Mother Goose rhyme

"Pussy cat, pussy cat,
What did you there?"
"I frightened a little mouse
Under her chair."

pictures by Michael Foreman

Round Is a Pancake

by Joan Sullivan

pictures by Frank Lamacchia

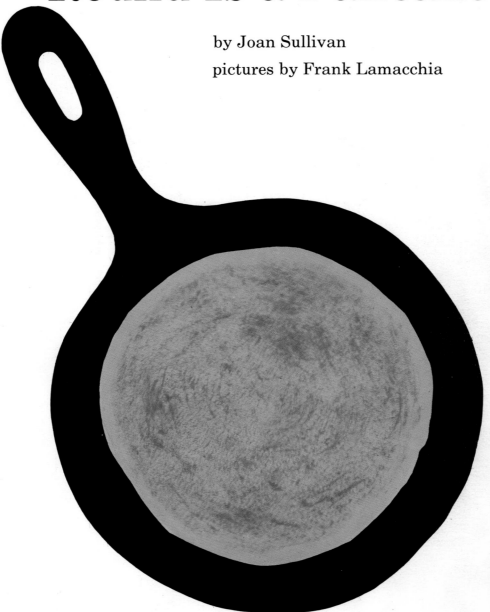

Round is a pancake,

Round is a plum,

Round is a doughnut,

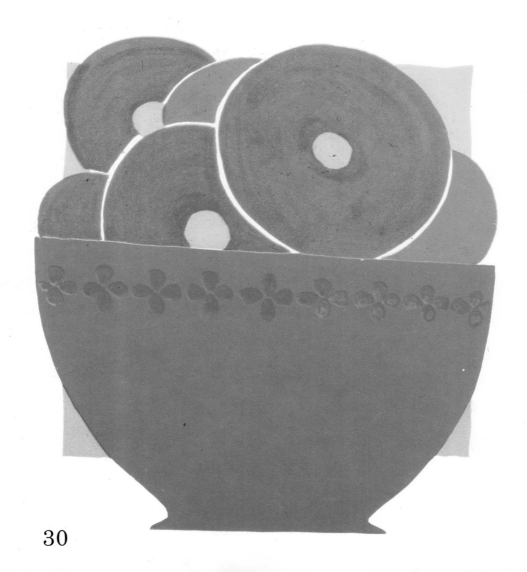

Round is a drum.

Round is a puppy
Curled up on a rug.

Round are the spots
On a wee ladybug.

Look all around,
On the ground, in the air,

You will find round things
Everywhere.

I Love You Little,

I love you lots,
My love for you
will fill 10 pots,
14 dishpans
12 teakettles
and
1 large bathtub
of precious metals.

an old chant adapted

Little Sister

photograph by Richard Erdoes

How Many Apples?

a chant
picture by Eric Carle

How many apples
Do you see?
Can you count them?
1, 2, 3.

How many green ones?
How many red?
Now eat an apple
And get to bed!

Dilly Dilly Piccalilli

Tell me something very silly.

There was a man,
  his name was Bert.

He ate the buttons off my shirt.

a rhyme by Clyde Watson
pictures by Wendy Watson

"Daddy is Home!" a story by David Blomquist, pictures by Sonia Lisker

"Daddy is home!

Daddy is home!

Daddy is home!

Daddy is home!"

"Look, Mother! Daddy's Home!"

"Hello, children!
Hello, Mother!"

"Hello, Daddy!"

"I brought you a surprise, children!"

"Where, Daddy, where?"

"Thank you, Daddy.
Thank you.

We love you, Daddy.
We love you, Mommy, too."

Hummingbirds
are like helicopters.
Their wings flutter faster
than the eye can see.
They can fly
straight up,
straight down,
straight forward,
straight backward,
even stand still
in mid-air
as they sip nectar
from flowers.

by Bill Martin Jr   picture by Bernard Martin

55

a song by Frank Silver and Irving Cohn
pictures by Kelly Oechsli

Yes! We have no bananas
we have no bananas today.

We have

and

and

and

and all kinds of
and say,

We have
old fashioned

Long Island . . . but—

57

Yes, we have no bananas,

We have no 🍌 today.

Here's a Picture for Storytelling

picture by Sal Murdocca

Happy Birthday, Henry!

a traditional rhyme
picture by Gilbert Riswold

Henry has a birthday,

We're so glad.

Let us see how many

He has had.

As we count the candles

We are told

   1, 2, 3, 4, 5, 6 . . .

Yes, the candles say

He's six years old.

adapted from a poem by Kate Greenaway
picture by John Rombola

Jump, Jump,
Jump all day.
Hurry back
Another way.

Jump,
Jump,
Jump all night,
Just because
The moon is bright.